A Balloon Adventure

by Dartford, Maidstone and Sittingbourne book club members
illustrated by Gaby Weigert

Beyond Words

London

First edition published 2016 by Books Beyond Words.

Text & illustrations © Books Beyond Words 2016.

No part of this book may be reproduced in any form, or by any means without prior permission in writing from the publisher.

ISBN 978-1-78458-082-7

British Library Cataloguing-in-Publication Data
A catalogue record for this book is available from the British Library.

Printed by Book Printing UK, Peterborough.

Books Beyond Words is a Community Interest Company registered in England and Wales (7557861).

St George's Hospital Charity is a registered charity (no. 241527).

Contents

Storyline

The following words are provided for readers and supporters who want some ideas about one possible story. Most readers make their own story up from the pictures.

1. Stuart and Zoe fly up high in their hot air balloon.

2. A big gust of wind catches them by surprise. It blows the balloon off course.

3. The balloon crash lands in a cornfield. Stuart is really fed up. A passerby sees it happen.

4. The passerby phones the police for help.

5. A police officer arrives. He has a rope in his car.

6. They tie the rope around the basket. They all pull and push as hard as they can.

7. The police officer fetches a pump from his car.

8. He uses the pump to blow up the balloon.

9. Oh dear. The pump pops out and all of the air comes out of the balloon.

10. The police officer tries again. Stuart and Zoe are excited. It's got to work this time!

11. The balloon flies up into the sky. Everyone waves goodbye.

12. They float over the cliffs, beaches and sea.

13. "Look!" says Zoe. Stuart takes a photo. They are in France.

14. The balloon flies over a huge ocean. Stuart and Zoe see dolphins swimming in the water.

15. Stuart and Zoe are in America. What a great holiday!

Pictures to colour for yourself

You can bring your own artistic talents to the story and colour some of the pictures for yourself on the next pages.

Felt tips work best for colouring these pictures.

Picture This

Valuing individual creativity is very important to our sense of well-being. This idea was at the centre of everything we did in this project and helped bring out the best in all of us.

Kent libraries in partnership with Beyond Words worked with self-advocates and artists to develop three innovative picture books. The storylines were developed through a series of drama workshops with self-advocates engaging in a story making process. Using drama to improvise scenes and develop stories for the artists to capture, we created three original picture books for people with learning disabilities.

Beyond Words' project team made 15 visits to nine Kent book clubs, holding drama workshops to invent the original stories. The artists drew the first set of pictures based on the drama sessions, and self-advocates then read and commented on them. The pictures were edited and redrawn in response to the feedback from the book clubs and readers in local day centres and activity groups.

Trialling the pictures several times across multiple visits to book clubs helped the artists to make the stories as clear and engaging as possible. Honouring the opinions and choices of people on the project has kept the book club readers' voices genuinely at the centre of the stories.

There has been a lot of laughter on this project and people have told us how much they have enjoyed taking part.

Related titles

A Day at the Beach (2016) by Deal, Dover and Folkestone book clubs, illustrated by Lucy Bergonzi. Friends Ellie, Nadya, Miles and Rob are spending a day at the seaside. They have fun swimming, building sandcastles, eating ice cream and subathing. But the friends soon meet a seagull determined to cause mischief.

A Night in Space (2016) by Edenbridge, Tonbridge and Tunbridge Wells book clubs, illustrated by Beth Aulton. Annie loves outer space. One night, Annie dreams that she flies to another planet and meets a friendly alien and some space explorers. It's up to Annie and the alien to help the space explorers find what they are looking for.

Ginger is a Hero (2015) by Beth Webb. Mary and her neighbour Mrs Hill don't get on. Mrs Hill gets really cross when her cat, Ginger, makes friends with Mary. But when Mrs Hill collapses at home, it's down to Mary and Ginger to save her life.

Beyond Words

To find out more about Beyond Words training and publications please visit our website:
www.booksbeyondwords.co.uk

Artist

Gaby Weigert studied Printed Textiles (BA Hons) at Glasgow School of Art and did an MA in Fine Art Printmaking at Camberwell College of Art. Her illustrations are a combination of print, paint and digital media. Gaby's website is www.gabyweigert.wix.com/amazingcreatures

Acknowledgments

A big thank you to the three book clubs who created the story. Dartford Peppercorns book club: Jimmy, Nick, Lilley, Sam, Rebecca, Grace and supporters Clair, Sue and Andrew. Maidstone book club: Debbie, Carole, Karen, Kevin, Peter, Joss, Andrew and supporters Sam, Charlotte, Tammy, Linda and Mark. Sittingbourne book club: Leigh, Gerard, Rosemary, Jessica, Stewart, Jamie, Lance and supporters Wendy and Tom.

Special thanks to Liz Taylor from Kent Libraries for her tireless support and for the initial idea that inspired this whole project.

Thank you to the book clubs, groups and day services who trialled the pictures: Dartford Peppercorns: Chris, Chloe, Joan, Barry, Amy, Taomi and Andrew; Everyday English Group Sittingbourne; Topaz Community Maidstone; North Kent Independent Advocacy Service; and Cliftonville Beyond Words book club.

We are grateful to Arts Council England for their generous funding of this project.

How to read this book

There is no right or wrong way to read this book. Remember it is not necessary to be able to read the words.

1. Some people are not used to reading books. Start at the beginning and read the story in each picture. Encourage the reader to hold the book themselves and to turn the pages at their own pace.

2. Whether you are reading the book with one person or with a group, encourage them to tell the story in their own words. You may think something different is happening in the pictures yourself, but that doesn't matter. Don't challenge the reader(s) or suggest their ideas are wrong.

3. You can help readers along by asking questions like:

- Who do you think that is?
- What is happening?
- How is he or she feeling?
- Do you ever feel like that?

4. You don't have to read the whole book in one sitting. Have fun with it: allow people time to chat about what they are reading and to follow the pictures at their own pace.

5. You can use the pictures as a storyboard for a drama group to create a play of the book.